IT'S NOT FINE TO SIT ON A PORCUPINE

NEAL ZETTER

troika books

To Liz, Chris and Becky
for their endless toleration and inspiration

Published by TROIKA BOOKS
First published 2016

Troika Books
Well House, Green Lane, Ardleigh CO7 7PD, UK
www.troikabooks.com

A CIP catalogue record for this book is available
from the British Library

ISBN 978-1-909991-28-6
1 2 3 4 5 6 7 8 9 10

Printed in Poland

Renewals

0333 370 4700

arena.yourlondonlibrary.net/
web/bromley

Bromley

THE LONDON BOROUGH
www.bromley.gov.uk

Please return/renew this item
by the last date shown.
Books may also be renewed by
phone and Internet.

Contents

It's Not Fine to Sit on a Porcupine

It's not fine to sit on a porcupine
Your day will turn nasty and rotten
You'll have holes in your pants
And there's quite a big chance
That his quills will stay stuck in your bottom

It's not fine to sit on a porcupine
You'll shoot like a star to the ceiling
And experience pain
From your toes to your brain
Then be left with a tingling feeling

Although the creature's cute and sweet
With button nose
And tiny feet
He'll stop you relaxing in your seat
Because . . .

It's not fine to sit on a porcupine
Please listen, take note of my warning
When you're touching those spines
You'll scream loudly and whine
And your bum will still ache in the morning

It's not fine to sit on a porcupine
That's true, I'm not joking or jesting
If you now ignore this
You'll end up with sore bits
So be careful where your rear is resting

There's No Such Thing as a Wazzock

There's no such thing as a Wazzock Mum said
As she turned the light off and tucked me in bed
Those shadows that shake must be all in my head
There's no such thing as a Wazzock

There's no such thing as a Wazzock you see
The creature that loves to eat children for tea
Though in the dark four eyes are following me
There's no such thing as a Wazzock

There's no such thing as a Wazzock it's true
That's why you'll not find them in cages in zoos
It's rumoured they're furry and indigo blue
There's no such thing as a Wazzock

There's no such thing as a Wazzock I know
As tall as a tree from its hat to its toe
With horns of a rhino and claws of a crow
There's no such thing as a Wazzock

There's no such thing as a Wazzock it seems
So I can sleep safely and have pleasant dreams
Why would I be woken by squawking and screams?
When there's no such thing as a Wazzock

Kids Love Ketchup

Kids love ketchup on their chips
Kids love ketchup on their crisps
Kids love ketchup on their eggs
Kids love ketchup on their bread

Kids love ketchup on baked beans
And to drown the taste of greens
Kids love ketchup though of course
Posh kids say 'tomato sauce'

Kids love ketchup on pork chops
Chicken, chocolate, lollipops
Kids love ketchup
they form queues
Just to watch
that ketchup
ooooooooooze

Kids love ketchup in meat pies
Make my bottle jumbo size
Kids love ketchup on their plates
It's the relish they most rate

Kids love ketchup on their hair
Hands, nose, clothes and everywhere
Kids love ketchup twenty-four seven
Like to live in ketchup heaven

Kids love ketchup on their cheese
Kids love ketchup freshly squeeeeeeeeeezed
Dig the red ketchuppy mess
Do kids love ketchup? Yes! Yes! Yes!

Bored Superhero

I'm a bored superhero
With nothing left to do
I've saved the Earth a hundred times
And distant planets too
Defeated every villain
And foiled their evil plans
No longer called to action
I'm not a busy man

I'm a bored superhero
Have you a job for me?
I'll help grannies crossing roads
Or rescue cats from trees
I'd rather face grave danger
And flex my muscles tight
Show off my mighty powers
Beat baddies in a fight

I'm a bored superhero
Now wearing normal clothes
With costume packed inside a box
I'm just another Joe
Nobody ever knows me
When I stroll into town
But I've made it a safer place
There's no crime to be found

I'm a bored superhero
So hire me if you like
I'll clean your house at triple speed
Or trace your stolen bike
Perform at children's parties
Or walk your dog for you
I'm a bored superhero
With nothing left to do

Angry Shopping Trolley

I am an angry shopping trolley
You guide me left and right
But I've got a bad attitude
So I go where I like
If you choose to use me
I'll eat and keep your pound
Then make you shake and then vibrate
While you move me around

I am an angry shopping trolly
A metal mean machine
Although my mates help customers
I'm awkward as can be
I knock into your kneecaps
I roll over your toes
Please bring a bag with you next time
And leave me here alone

I'm an angry shopping trolley
Not your supermarket pal
Why don't you buy your groceries
Somewhere else inside this mall?
I bash the other trolleys
And give them bad headaches
It's not my fault I don't possess
A steering wheel or brakes

I gripe and get real grumpy
When kids sit in my seat
While parents push me down the aisle
And cram me full of fruit . . . salad . . . biscuits . . .
    drinks . . . vegetables . . . fish . . . crisps . . . and meat
Take me to the checkout – now!
Or I'll suddenly stop
I'm an angry shopping trolley
Who doesn't want to SHOP!

Fire Alarm

Beep, beep, beep, beep
"Pens down, books down"
Beep, beep, beep, beep
"March to the playground"

Beep, beep, beep, beep
"Leave bags, coats, hats"
Beep, beep, beep, beep
"Form a queue, don't chat"

Beep, beep, beep, beep
"Walk down the corridor"
Beep, beep, beep, beep
"Walk down the back stairs"

Beep, beep, beep, beep
"By the gate – two rows"
Beep, beep, beep, beep
"Just a drill? Who knows?"

Beep, beep, beep, beep
"Answer when your name's called"
Beep, beep, beep, beep
"Danny – drop the football!"

Beep, beep, beep, beep
"Anyone seen Charlotte?"
Beep, beep, beep, beep
"She's stuck in the toilet!"

Beep, beep, beep, beep
"Wait and wait and wait and wait"
Beep, beep, beep, beep
"Dinner time will be late"

Beep, beep, beep, beep
"The fire brigade's in school"
Beep, beep, beep, beep
"No fire found at all"

Beep, beep, beep, beep
"Walk up the back stairs"
Beep, beep, beep, beep
"Walk up the corridor"

Beep, beep, beep, beep
Teacher said "Two out of ten..."
Beep, beep, beep, beep
"Tomorrow we will try again"

Beep, beep, beep, beep . . .

Mister Poetry Man

Here comes a man
With a pen in his hand
Rhythms and rhymes at his command
To build a sandcastle
You need sand
But who'd you need to write a poem?
Mister Poetry Man

Here comes a man
Guaranteed to inspire
Spreading sunshine and creating a smile
To eat a jam sandwich
You need jam
But who'd you need to write a poem?
Mister Poetry Man

Here comes a man
With a million ideas
Using verse to help sadness disappear
To drink a can of Coke
You need a can
But who'd you need to write a poem?
Mister Poetry Man

Here comes a man
To make dreams come true
And a rainbow sky if you're feeling blue
To take a tram ride
You need a tram
But who'd you need to write a poem?
Mister Poetry Man

Here comes a man
With a magical touch
Words pour from his mouth
You can't get enough
If you like 'fantastic'
You will be a fan
But who'd you need to write a poem?
Mister Poetry Man

Have a Laugh

Have a chuckle
Have a giggle
Till your belly bobs and jiggles
Go on – act completely daft
Have a laugh
Ha! Ha! Ha!

You'll feel jolly
You'll feel cheery
When your day
is dull and dreary
Don't sing in
your shower
or bath
Have a laugh
Ha! Ha! Ha!

Ha! Ha! Ha!
He! He! He!
Try a bit of comedy
Laugh, laugh, laugh
Have a laugh
Ha! Ha! Ha!

Make a smirk
Make a smile
Keep on grinning all the while
Like hyenas
Not giraffes
Have a laugh
Ha! Ha! Ha!

Why be grumpy?
Why be moody?
When you're down and bored and broody
Reach out to your happy half
Have a laugh
Ha! Ha! Ha!

Ha! Ha! Ha!
He! He! He!
Melt away your misery
Laugh, laugh, laugh
Have a laugh
Ha! Ha! Ha!

An Alien Lives at Number 42

A most unusual creature dwells next door
Put your ear to my wall you can hear him snore
Made of plastic
And elastic
His favourite meal is monster stew
There's an alien who lives at number 42

He has a giant TV aerial growing from his head
"Greetings Earth man" was the first thing he said
He's podgy
And splodgy
Wears a size 16 shoe
There's an alien who lives at number 42

He's really quite a friendly Martian chap
Who does't want to conquer us or anything like that
He's rubbery
And blubbery
I pinch myself but know it's true
There's an alien who lives at number 42

You can see his flying saucer parked outside
Give him three jelly babies he'll take you for a ride
He's spongy
And grungy
I don't know his name – do you?
There's an alien who lives at number 42

He bought a one-way ticket from outer space
So he could reside with the human race
He's kind of tall
But kind of small
Would you find him at the zoo?
No – he's the alien who lives at number 42

My Dad's Boots

My dad's boots are big and brown
My dad's boots stomp on the ground

My dad's boots are shiny clean
My dad's boots are size 13

My dad's boots are strong and tough
My dad's boots are hard and rough

My dad's boots have thick black laces
My dad's boots take him to places

My dad's boots are really smart
My dad's boots are works of art

My dad's boots built in Beijing
My dad's boots fit for a king

My dad's boots glide over mud
My dad's boots go THUD! THUD! THUD!

My dad's boots are made of leather
Dad and boots always together

When I'm old Dad I want to
Own a pair of boots like you

I love my dad's boots

Wet Play

Children bouncing off the walls
Breaking each and every rule
Noise and din rapidly growing
Teachers' stress levels are showing
Tables, chairs wrecked in a mess
Scattered dominoes and chess

Games out
Books away
Everyone shouts
"Wet play!"

Eat your lunch then class again
'Cause outside it's pouring rain
Football pitches drenched and muddy
Sandpits soaking, drowned and flooded
Drier times are so much better
It's no fun when weather's wetter

Autumn clouds
Dark and grey
Thunder, lightning
"Wet play!"

Pupils bored, nothing to do
Jump about like kangaroos
In a hyperactive state
More a battle than a break
Miss is yelling "Stop! Stop! Stop!"
Praying soon it's one o'clock

Summer sun?
Not today
So what's instead?
"Wet play!"

Padlock the Fridge

I put a padlock on our fridge
Securing it from all my kids
Who really are a greedy bunch
They scoff my dinner, stuff my lunch
They nibble cheese and next of course
They're slurping down the chocolate sauce
The custard's been consigned to history
Though where it went to is no mystery

The apple pie has missing bites
While ice cream disappears from sight
And yoghurts vanish just like that
They hog the ham but leave the fat
The baked bean can that was half-full
Has no beans left in it at all
They gobble up my weekly shopping
"Where's the plate with that pork chop in?"

Cola, milkshakes, fruit juice drinks
I don't find poured into the sink
Then how come that the shelves are bare?
Why is no peanut butter spare?
Fingerprints in margarine!
"Who consumed the squirty cream?"
Though you bet it's not a grown up
Younger voices never own up

Strawberry shortcake – always stolen
Melons found with giant holes in
Bacon rashers go AWOL
Sausageless are sausage rolls
Yes my fridge empties overnight
Now chains around it are fixed tight
But I hold keys so I am fine
At last its entire contents . . . are mine!

Soap!

It makes your skin feel smooth and nice
While killing off your fleas and lice
As slippy as a slippery slope
'You can't beat a bar of
'Soap!'

Removing grease between your toes
And grime that gathers round your nose
If your personal hygiene's a joke
'You can't beat a bar of
'Soap!'

Little babies – always enjoy it
Teenagers – always avoid it
More bubbles than a can of Coke
'You can't beat a bar of
'Soap!'

Rub and scrub, bring out those suds
Bash stubborn stains and murder mud
Make a lather till you're thoroughly soaked
'You can't beat a bar of
'Soap!'

Don't tip or drip it in your drink
Use plenty if you smell or stink
Hippopotamuses how do they cope?
'You can't beat a bar of
'Soap!'

Put it on your 'orrible oily bits
Add it to disgusting soily bits
If your dad is a dirty bloke
Tell him "You can't beat a bar of
"Soap!"

In winter when it's cold you're freezing
Coughing, croaking, wheezing, sneezing
Cry out and give a loud whoop
'You can't beat a bowl of
'Soup!'

I'm a Lollipop Man

I'm a Lollipop Man
I stand in the road
I'm a Lollipop Man
I know the Green Cross Code

I'm a Lollipop Man
I look left and right
I'm a Lollipop Man
My coat's long and white

I'm a Lollipop Man
Read my big round sign
I'm a Lollipop Man
I keep the cars in line

I'm a Lollipop Man
I will help you cross
I'm a Lollipop Man
I'm the traffic's boss

I'm a Lollipop Man
Protecting all of you
I'm a Lollipop Man
That's what I'm here to do

I'm a Lollipop Man
I make transport stop
I'm a Lollipop Man
With my big lollipop

I'm a Lollipop Man

You Can't Take a Goldfish
for a Walk

You can stick a cork in an elephant's trunk
Put a hippo on a diet to lose weight
You can book a meeting with a tortoise too
Though expect him to be late
You could clean the teeth of a crocodile's smile
Teach the shyest parrot to talk
But when choosing a pet
Please don't forget
You can't take a goldfish for a walk

You can instruct a flamingo to win at bingo
And a pig to keep out the mud
Brief a vampire bat informing him that
It's so uncool to suck blood
Tell vultures, seagulls, buzzards and eagles
That it's very impolite to squawk
But as they swapped their limbs
For a bunch of fins
You can't take a goldfish for a walk

You can help a hyena split his sides laughing
Tie a rattlesnake in a knot
Have a race with a cheetah (though he's bound to beat ya)

Then paint out a leopard's spots
The chimpanzee who's coming to tea
Could eat with a knife and fork
But when you buy aquatic creatures
Remember this one feature
You can't take a goldfish for a walk

You can tell a chinchilla to sit on a gorilla
Force a cow to go 'woof' not 'moo'
Enquire if a wallaby would one day wanna be
Converted to a kangaroo
Though they're omnivores beg bears not to gnaw
On beef or lamb or pork
But as they much prefer the water
This simple fact will never alter
You can't take a goldfish for a walk

Don't be dim
They only like to swim
So you can't
    take a goldfish
    for a walk

Orange Man

*(About my friend who uses sunbeds and spray tans
to fool everyone into thinking he has travelled
all over the world for his holidays)*

He was an orange man
Had a fake suntan
Said he went to Saint Tropez
Lied about his holiday
Booked the tanning shop instead
Lazed on a sunbed

Never been to Africa
Never been to India
Never seen America
Never seen Jamaica

He was an orange man
Had a fake suntan
Chose to stay every day
Under ultraviolet rays
Made his skin feel just like leather
Though he'd never seen hot weather

Never been to Italy
Never been to Turkey
Never been to Portugal
Never been to Spain at all

He was an orange man
Had a fake suntan
Changed his colour overnight
Though certain bits remained white

Never been to Tonga
Never been to China
Never been to Greece you know
Never been to Mexico

He was an orange man
Had a fake suntan
Didn't need transport
Didn't need a passport
Had a very strange look
Like a chicken overcooked

Never been to Cuba
Not seen Madagascar
Never been to Pakistan
Israel, Egypt or Japan

He was an orange man
Had a fake suntan

Minotaur
in My Minestrone Soup

The Minotaur's swimming in my minestrone soup
Dipping, diving
Looping the loop
Sploshing, splashing
Kicking his hooves
Doing water aerobics to the latest dance grooves

He's half a bull
And half a man
Not on the label of the can

So it was quite a big surprise
When he appeared before my eyes
Groaning
Growling
Howling
Floating in my liquid feast
An Italian dish invaded by the beast of Ancient Greece

He's chewing on my celery
He's pointing both his horns at me
Spits carrots and sweetcorn at me
Why was nobody warning me?

I know this guy is legendary
But tell me what do you think you'd do
With a mythological monster doing backstroke in your stew?

The Minotaur's in my minestrone bowl
Escaped from the labyrinth's deep, dark hole
Zipping in and out the pasta
Showing me his teeth
My vegetarian meal demolished by a hunk of beef

This creature who dines on human flesh
Is dressed in just his trunks and his vest
Incredibly weird but it's the honest truth
The Minotaur's swimming in my minestrone soup

Mr Teacher is Our Teacher

Mr Teacher is our teacher
"It's tricky to explain"
He told us when he taught us
So he told us once again

"I'm your teacher, Mr Teacher
"You say 'teacher' twice
"I was born a Teacher
"Been a Teacher all my life"

Mr Teacher is our teacher
It messes with our brains
Though teacher is the job he does
It's also his last name

He's married to a teacher
So she's called 'Teacher' too
Mrs Teacher is a teacher
Also teaching at our school

They've got two Teacher children
Who may grow up to teach
A total of four Teachers teaching
Would be really neat!

But now we're even more confused
'Cause Mr Teacher said
"A new Headteacher starts tomorrow . . .
"And her name's 'Mrs Head'!"

The Wrong Side of the Bed

Ben got out the wrong side of the bed
Like a big bruised bear with a super sore head
He cursed
He swore
Kicked wildly at his door
Books, clothes and toys were strewn across his floor

He stomped down to breakfast
Was rude to his dad
Though Mum greeted him "Good morning"
He snapped "No, bad!"
Madder than mad
Like a raging bull
Losing his cool
The only colour he saw was blood red
When Ben got out the wrong side of the bed

His anger rose as he marched into school
He was caught throwing carrots in the dinner hall
He refused to hand his spelling test in
Stuffed his history homework into the bin
Uptighter than uptight
The whole world was wrong
And only he was right
He barged into a year six boy and then picked a fight
'GRRRRRRRRRRRRRR!' was the most frequent word he said
When Ben got out the wrong side of the bed

Normally he was a calm, quiet lad
Conscientious, sweet and charming
But today he was an exploding volcano
Dangerous and alarming
Spitting molten lava far and wide
After getting out of his bed from the wrong side

His teacher handed him detention
His Head threatened him with suspension
Then summoned his parents for a serious chat
Firmly and sternly reiterating that
Ben's behaviour was utterly regrettable
Completely reprehensible
Totally unacceptable
He was to be placed on a final warning
The old Ben was required to return to class next morning

When back home his folks screamed
"Shameful! Disgraceful! Out of our sight!"
So he stormed upstairs to his room
Switched off the light
As Ben's angry day ended with
No computer, no TV, no pocket money, no tea
And a very early night

What's the moral?
Never get out the wrong side of your bed
Just count to ten
Turn over
And get out the other side instead

My Dad Thinks He's Cool

My dad thinks he's cool
But he's not cool at all

He embarrasses me at the school gate
Attempting to speak street slang to all of my mates
Dad – you're not eleven, you've turned thirty-eight

My dad thinks he's cool
But he's not cool at all

It's ever so painful when he sings along
To all of the latest Top 40 songs
He whines out of tune getting all the words wrong

My dad thinks he's cool
But he's not cool at all

He wears new fashions to try to impress
Though under his shirt you'll see a string vest
He'd score a big fat zero in the `How Cool R U?' test

My dad thinks he's cool
But he's not cool at all

He tries to play football with the rest of my team
His skills on the pitch are the worst I've ever seen
Out-tackled and out-dribbled by girls of thirteen

My dad thinks he's cool
But he's not cool at all

So he'll never beat me at computer gaming
Despite hours and hours of meticulous training
I'm beating all records but he's doing my brain in

My dad thinks he's cool
But he's not cool at all

And if you're reading this Dad
    I hope you understand
Why I'd like all these mad things
    you do to be banned
I love you just as you are so please
    – act like a man!

My dad thinks he's cool
But he's not cool at all

Zooteacher

There's a teacher in a cage at my local zoo
Doing all the things schoolteachers do
Shouting at the parrots every time they squawk
Asking racing cheetahs not to run but walk

Handing out homework to the clever cockatoos
Shouting at the wallabies fighting kangaroos
Babbling to the badgers 'bout their ABC
While hanging from the branch of a tall, tall tree

He's such an incredible zoo exhibit
Of all the creatures he's the best one in it

There's a teacher in a cage at my local zoo
Doing all the things schoolteachers do
Sitting in the straw on the floor on his own
Drinking coffee and playing with his mobile phone

Telling off the hyenas for laughing too much
Yelling at the monkeys throwing monkey nuts
Explaining to the pigs why they shouldn't eat ham
Helping rats to read and pass their maths exam

He's the first zooteacher that I've ever met
I want to take him home and keep him as our pet

There's a teacher in a cage at my local zoo
Doing all the things schoolteachers do

Mammoth on the Underground

There's a mammoth on the Underground
Causing quite a crush
There's a mammoth on the Underground
Making such a fuss
There's a mammoth on the Underground
Sitting on ten seats
There's a mammoth on the Underground
Check those hairy feet

There's a mammoth on the Underground
Blocking carriage doors
There's a mammoth on the Underground
Letting out a "ROOOOAAAARRRRRRR!"
There's a mammoth on the Underground
Trunk upon my lap
There's a mammoth on the Underground
I warned him "Mind the gap!"

There's a mammoth on the Underground
Thump! Thump! Thump!
There's a mammoth on the Underground
Stomp! Stomp! Stomp!
There's a mammoth on the Underground
Mash! Mash! Mash!
There's a mammoth on the Underground
Crash! Crash! Crash!

There's a mammoth on the Underground
Weighing twenty tons
There's a mammoth on the Underground
Scoffing current buns
There's a mammoth on the Underground
Two titanic tusks
There's a mammoth on the Underground
Can't he take the bus?

There's a mammoth on the Underground
Got on at Finsbury Park
There's a mammoth on the Underground
He's off to Marble Arch
There's a mammoth on the Underground
Slowing down my train
There's a mammoth on the Underground
Shout it out again

There's a mammoth on the Underground
Thump! Thump! Thump!
There's a mammoth on the Underground
Stomp! Stomp! Stomp!
There's a mammoth on the Underground
Mash! Mash! Mash!
There's a mammoth on the Underground
Crash! Crash! Crash!

I'm an Ant

I'm an ant
I'm a tiny ant
I think it's cool
To be so small
Unlike a giraffe who's very tall
Or a huge elephant
What am I?
I'm an ant

I'm a tiny ant
I crawl in pavement cracks
Under closed doors
Up your garden path
On your old apple cores
And then I get into your pants
What am I?
I'm an ant

I'm a tiny ant
I think it's wise
To be a millimetre in size
Then I can hide from hungry flies
Please join me in my rant
What am I?
I'm an ant

I'm a tiny ant
I move through mud
Live under rocks
Walk about in grass
And in your smelly socks
Be careful where you stamp
You might tread on me
What am I?
I'm an ant

I'm a tiny ant
That's what I am
I'm gonna steal your strawberry jam
For tea
So give me an 'A' an 'N' and a 'T'
I can see you
But you can't see me
What am I?
I'm an ant

When I am Prime Minister

When I am Prime Minister
You'll have homework by the ton
Maths lessons will quadruple
And I'll fine you for having fun

In the Tower of London dungeon
I'll imprison the Royal Family
On pound coin heads you'll find me instead
And all kids will be forced to eat greens

At my residence, 10 Downing Street
I'll rest with my feet up
While passing laws guaranteeing for sure
Just my team can win the Cup

Those nations I find annoying
My armies will invade in a flash
Then march their way round to your house
To confiscate your cash

Your screensavers and wallpapers
Will have to bear my face
Holidays and birthdays too
Will vanish without a trace

My special police will steal your sweets
Toys, TVs, books and games
I'll tax anyone who speaks or laughs
Or dares misspell my name

Each weekday you'll hear only classical music
Only opera at the weekends
These things I also promise to do
If I became PM

With my hand holding the master switch
I'll control the entire country
So tell me in next month's election please . . .
Will YOU be voting for me?

Bungee-jumping Grandad

"Geronimo!"
You'll hear him cry
While zooming off into the sky
He catapults towards the ground
He ricochets towards the clouds
Upon his head are five big bumps
'Cause Grandad loves to bungee jump

"Look out!
"I'm 90 but don't care"
He yells while falling through the air
My nan is now a nervous wreck
The doctor says he'll break his neck
Just like a kangaroo in flight
I watch and cross my fingers tight

"Yipeeee!"
He's leaping from a tree
Or from a hotel balcony
Most pensioners like peace and quiet
Yet he likes deadly sports and heights
He plummets down, then bounces up
He wants to win the Bungee Cup

Booooiiiiing!
He dangles from a cliff
If I was him I'd be scared stiff
Though here at home we call him 'Pa'
On the Internet he's 'superstar'
Will he crash into an aeroplane?
Will he splash into the pouring rain?
Will he tumble to Earth
    with a splat?
Will he squash and flatten
    next door's cat?
Will he soar away to outer
    space?
Will he disappear
    without a trace?
Will he crash-land
    with a mighty
    thump?
Who knows what
    will happen . . .
On Grandad's next
    bungee jump

Waiting for the Bus

I'm waiting for the bus
Although I'm in a rush
Today's being spent
Stuck like cement
Waiting for the bus

I'm feeling very stressed
Annoyed and quite depressed
I feel my nose 'n'
Toes have frozen
Waiting for the bus

I'm growing old and grey
Time slowly ticks away
Moaning, snoring
Very boring
Waiting for the bus

It's number 32
The bus for which I queue
I've stood for hours
Sprung roots like flowers
Waiting for the bus

I'm now extremely late
And in an angry state
Complaining
Great – it's raining!
Waiting for the bus

Perhaps to get ahead
I'll go by train instead
The thing to do?
Catch that choo-choo
Waiting for the train

Killer Dog

My dog would kill for chicken
My dog would kill for cheese
He'd kill for a lasagne
And also rice and peas

My dog would kill for apple cores
My dog would kill for chips
Steak, pork, ham or minted lamb
Cause him to lick his lips

My dog would kill for carrots (raw)
And biscuits without doubt
My dog would kill for cucumber
Mayonnaise and deep-fried trout

My dog would kill for chocolate bars
(Although they do him harm)
The thought of jelly in his belly
Rings his dog alarm

My dog would kill for scrambled eggs
My dog would kill for beef
If you cook bacon sandwiches
He'll slobber through his teeth

My dog would kill for noodle soup
And spicy vindaloo
My dog would kill for lemon curd
For bean and lentil stew

But my dog is a sweet dog really
So don't worry about any of that
He would never, ever hurt you at all . . .
Unless you are a cat!

Match of the Day

We hide under the table
We cower behind the chair
We hear words we've never heard
As swearing fills the air

The TV screen's been damaged
Remote control is mashed
The living room's a battlefield
The furniture's been trashed

Dad's blood pressure is rising
Mum tells him to calm down
Blue veins are bulging from his head
His heart begins to pound

While steam pours out his nostrils
His feet stamp on the floor
A hundred crazed gorillas
Would shrivel at his roar

There's dinner on the carpet
And beer spilt down his jeans
He turns a shade of purple
Yellow, orange, red and green

He writhes around in agony
Yells "I can't take no more!"
Though I thought sport was just for fun
To him it's just for war

Our windows are all broken
Our satellite dish is smashed
All extremely annoying
But Dad's way of enjoying
Another football match

My Carpet Spot

This is my carpet spot
My bottom rests upon it
This is my carpet spot
Don't put your bottom on it

My friends are either side of me
Together we learn A, B, C
And science, maths and history

This is my carpet spot
Shaped like a perfect square
This is my carpet spot
The spot I never share

I do not need a chair at all
When I am in my class at school
'Cause sitting here is really cool

This is my carpet spot
Fifty centimetres by fifty centimetres
This is my carpet spot
Where I listen to my teachers

There is no better place to be
My desert island in the sea
This seat's reserved – but just for me
'Cause this is my carpet spot

This is my carpet spot
This is my carpet spot
This is my carpet spot!

Z

It's not easy being the letter Z
I'm always last when the alphabet's read
I wish I was a C an F or a P instead
But I'm not
I'm the letter Z

I'm zigzag-shaped like a lightning bolt
Or a capital N on its side
Though you don't find me joining many words
I'm really a friendly guy
(Well that's what other letters have said)
I'm the letter Z

I'm in 'zip' and 'zap' and 'zebra' too
In a 'pizza' I appear twice
I'm often put in place of an S
For example in `recogniZe'
Especially in the USA
Where `zee' is what they always say
When they speak of me
Who gives the buzzzzzzzzz sound to a bee
That's flying round your head?
I do
I'm the letter Z

I live far, far away
From the letter A
But next door to the Y
I'm not in-between the two
Like the letter Q
I've no dot like a small letter i
And no symmetry like an O
If all the letters stood in order in a row
I'd be the last you'd get to know
I come out of your mouth or nose with a zzzzzzzzzzzzzzzzzzzzzzzzz
When you snore in your bed
Because I'm the letter Z
I am the letter Z

How Many Sleeps?

How many sleeps till my next birthday?
How many sleeps till our summer holiday?
How many sleeps till my hair turns grey?

How many days?
How many weeks?
How many sleeps?
Zzzzzzzzzzzzzzzzzzzzzzzzzzzzzzzzzzzzzzzzzzzzzzzzzz

How many sleeps till I can write my own name?
How many sleeps till Christmas comes again?
How many sleeps till my football team wins a game?

How many days?
How many weeks?
How many sleeps?
Zzzzzzzzzzzzzzzzzzzzzzzzzzzzzzzzzzzzzzzzzzzzzzzzzz

How many sleeps till I can stay up real late?
How many sleeps till I can ride my roller skates?
How many sleeps when a tortoise hibernates?

How many days?
How many weeks?
How many sleeps?
Zzzzzzzzzzzzzzzzzzzzzzzzzzzzzzzzzzzzzzzzzzzzzzz

How many sleeps till I buy my new shoes?
How many sleeps till I can spell 'Kalamazoo'?
How many sleeps till I stop asking you?

How many days?
How many weeks?
How many sleeps?
Zzzzzzzzzzzzzzzzzzzzzzzzzzzzzzzzzzzzzzzzzzzzzzzzz

Robot Teacher, 3018

(What would teachers be like in the next millennium?)

She's a nightmare not a dream
Colder than the coldest ice cream
Rules the class like a tyrannical queen
A fully automated metal machine
Our robot teacher
Of 3018

A giant computer for a brain
Long iron springs for hair
Laser eyes that burn like fire
Mess around – if you dare!
You'll be fried medium rare
Unemotional and mean
Our robot teacher
Of 3018

We call her Mrs Nutsnbolts
Her skin is silver foil
Her arms and legs are four steel spears
She don't drink coffee only oil
Full of wires, plugs and coils
And her face is a TV screen
Our robot teacher
Of 3018

As strict as a sergeant major
Handing homework out each night
Runs off the mains and batteries
Memory? A zillion gigabytes
Her swivel head keeps you in sight
You would wish you'd never met her
Old-style teachers are much better
A more terrifying creation will never be seen
Than our robot teacher
Of 3018

The Medical Room

Damaged superheroes
Mix with injured football stars
Poor Ruth
Lost a tooth
Kyle crashed his imaginary car
(Miss says it won't leave a scar)

Chaos and calamity
Like a night in A&E
Counting every casualty
I'm sure we'll see you soon
In the Medical Room

Rick was sick
On the floor
Priya's pen top stuck in her ear
Bella bumped into a door
An angry wasp stung Robert's rear
Kelly's crying floods of tears
Jojo's in a state of panic
Bitten on the nose by Janet

If your condition gets much worse
Join the queue to meet the nurse
I'm sure we'll see you soon
In the Medical Room

Katie's cut's a minor scratch
Ali has a nosebleed
William wants an eye patch
Sonia swallowed hamster feed
Yasmin's yelling "Plaster cast!"
But makes do with Elastoplast
Tia's bruised toe's turning green
Debbie's such a drama queen – and wow she can shout and scream!
It's a mad and manic scene

Walking wounded wait in line
Dying or simply trying to avoid lesson time?
No need to dial 999
Everyone will be just fine
I'm sure we'll see you soon
In the Medical Room

OJ

OJ, OJ
Good for you, good for me
It tastes so great, full of vitamin C
Pure ready-ripe oranges picked from a tree
OJ, OJ
Good for you, good for me

OJ, OJ
In a bottle or pack
Perfect with breakfast, lunch or a snack
If you bought me a cola I'd say "Take it back"
I want OJ, OJ
In a bottle or pack

OJ, OJ
One of your five a day
For a fitter, happier, healthier way
It'll keep you young, stop your hair going grey
OJ, OJ
One of your five a day

OJ, OJ
Mmmmm – freshly squeezed
Buy it smooth or with bits in if you please
What stops a cough and prevents a sneeze?
OJ, OJ
Mmmmm – freshly squeezed

So what's the drink you're going to choose?
It's got to be
OJ, OJ
OJ, OJ
OJ, OJ
OJ, OJ
OJ, OJ
OJ, OJ
Orange juice!

Crazy Old Uncle

Everyone has a crazy old uncle
An extremely eccentric relation
With a tiny screw or small wire loose
Like a slightly out of tune music radio station

A little bit peculiar
A little bit strange
A little bit weird
A little bit deranged

Wearing clothes from the 1970s
Plus a wobbly wig on his head
He makes you laugh
Needs a really good bath
Always mending broken things in his garden shed

Everyone has a crazy old uncle
You're proud of him though he's quite potty
Drives a rusty scooter
Owns a Stone Age computer
Spends weekends at Waterloo Station trainspotting

A little bit of a fruitcake
A little bit of an oddball
A little bit of a joker
Clowns around like a fool
Yet you love his visits 'cause he's still kinda cool

He can make a pound coin disappear
Pick eggs from your pockets and behind your ears
Brings you sweets and treats
Smells of wine and beer
He's everyone's crazy old uncle

Born centuries ago in Victorian times
Drives you nuts with silly jokes and sillier rhymes
He's one of a kind
A most unusual find
He's everyone's crazy old uncle

Yes everyone has a crazy old uncle
My nephews and nieces agree
But nodding their heads
Each one of them said
Their crazy old uncle was . . .
. . . Me!

The World's Worst Toilet

There's a huge crack in the bowl
Don't go there
There's no paper on the roll
Don't go there

Severed hinges on the door
Don't go there
Shattered tiles on the floor
Don't go there

There's an evil-smelling whiff
Don't go there
Broken seat and busted lid
Don't go there

The wallpaper is peeling
Don't go there
Check the cockroach on the ceiling
Don't go there

There's no key to turn the lock
Don't go there
And the pipe's completely blocked
Don't go there

The light has blown a fuse
Don't go there
The air freshener's all used
Don't go there

Someone stole the toilet brush
Don't go there
Once you've done
    you cannot flush
Don't go there

It's the place that
    you most dread
So keep calm and
    cross your legs
Wait until you're
    home instead
What's the warning
    that I said?
Don't go there!

Orangutang, atang, atang, atang, atang, atang

Who's swinging on that tree
Eats fruit and veg for tea?
The orange one that's lots of fun who children queue to see

Orangutang, atang, atang, atang, atang, atang
Orangutang, atang, atang, atang, atang, atang

With arms extremely long
Huge muscles, super-strong
He says his second cousin's the gorilla called King Kong

Orangutang, atang, atang, atang, atang, atang
Orangutang, atang, atang, atang, atang, atang

He's jumping up and down
Fists thumping on the ground
He loves to play so every day he's monkeying around

Orangutang, atang, atang, atang, atang, atang
Orangutang, atang, atang, atang, atang, atang

His home is way out East
The cleverest of beasts
He picks his nose, he bites his toes, then scratches all his fleas

Orangutang, atang, atang, atang, atang, atang
Orangutang, atang, atang, atang, atang, atang

He likes to beat his chest
Tries so hard to impress
Of all the apes you've ever met who'd you think is the best?

Orangutang, atang, atang, atang, atang, atang
Orangutang, atang, atang, atang, atang, atang

Orangutang, atang, atang, atang, atang, atang
Orangutang, atang, atang, atang, atang, atang

Shoelaces

Oh my shoelaces
You really drive me nuts
Although I want you undone
I'm told to do you up

I'd rather let you hang down
Prefer it if you dangled
I don't care you're in a mess
Or get all tied and tangled

It's cool to see you flopping
And looking longer too
Yet when I make you stay that way
There's such a hullabaloo

People warn me "You'll trip up
"Fall flat upon your face"
Though I say "Fashion statement"
My teacher yells "Disgrace!"

I could secure you with two bows
Or maybe double knots
Or pull you very tightly
But that might hurt – a lot

The truth is I'm just lazy
So stop doing in my head
When I next buy a pair of shoes
I'll choose Velcro instead

Catch the Flea!

Who is making your dog scratch? That's me
Who is making your cat itch? That's me
I can hop into your ear
I can crawl down your back
I can hide in a crevice
Be concealed in a crack
You won't spot me easily
I'm a flea, flea, flea, flea, flea – catch me!

Who is bouncing in your bed? That's me
Who is walking 'cross your head? That's me
I can drive you to despair
Make you fidget like you're crazy
Build my home inside your carpet
Splash and swim around your gravy
I'm your worst enemy
I'm a flea, flea, flea, flea, flea – catch me!

Who is tickling your toes? That's me
Who is wiggling your nose? That's me
Microscopic and minute
Miniature and minuscule
Elephants are extra big
While I am extra small
Such a tiny entity
I'm a flea, flea, flea, flea, flea – catch me!

Who is biting on your skin? That's me
Who is nibbling your chin? That's me
Jumping like a kangaroo
I'm a parasitic pest
You pour powder down your neck
If you feel me in your vest
Far too wee for you to see
I'm a flea, flea, flea, flea, flea – catch me!

You say I'm a nasty bug but I beg to disagree
I'm a flea, flea, flea, flea, flea – catch me!

If I Was a Spy

If I was a spy
I'd be a master of disguise
If I was a spy
I'd wear dark glasses on my eyes

If I was a spy
I'd sneak 'round secret places
If I was a spy
I'd hide cameras in suitcases

If I was a spy
I'd be an ace code-cracker
If I was a spy
I'd catch computer hackers

If I was a spy
I'd protect and serve my country
If I was a spy
Evil governments would hunt me

If I was a spy
Bad guys couldn't beat me
If I was a spy
No villain could defeat me

If I was a spy
You'd have no way of knowing
Because if I was a spy
I wouldn't tell you in this poem

An Amazing, Alliterative,
Incredible Insect Invasion

Big buzzing bees blagged my bananas
Hornets hid half of my ham
Six scary spiders scoffed my spicy sausages
Four flies filched my fruit flan

Ants ate all my apples (as always)
Crazed crickets crunched my carrot crisps
Beetles bit bits of my brown bread
Chiggers cheerfully chewed my chips

While wiggly worms whipped my walnuts
Roaches removed and ran away with my rolls
Many maggots munched my mango, Mum
Twenty-two tiny ticks took my toast

That perfect picnic I precisely planned
A wonderful one-off occasion
Was decimated, demolished and destroyed
By an amazing, alliterative, incredible insect invasion

There's a Dead Baked Bean
in My Microwave

There's a dead baked bean in my microwave
Playing at hide and seek
He has bits of blue on him
Don't suck or chew on him
He's been lying there for three weeks

There's a dead baked been in my microwave
Squashed and flat out on his back
I'm desperately itching
To lose him from my kitchen
He's far too unfit for a snack

There's a dead baked bean in my microwave
Lurking alone by himself
Haunts me like a ghost
Don't eat him on toast
He's likely to damage your health

There's a dead baked bean in my microwave
Wedged in the crack by the door
He's not a nice fella
He's got salmonella
I've cooked him at least twice before

There's a dead baked bean in my microwave
Congealed in tomato sauce
Fried, frazzled and old he
Is manky and mouldy
My stomach is turning and churning because . . .

There's a dead baked bean in my microwave
As dead as a dead bean can be
I'm scared to go near him
I secretly fear him
So I'll stick with cheese salad for tea

Down the Side of the Sofa

You got rubbish want to hide it?
Where's the secret place to slide it?
Down the side of the sofa . . .

Old socks
Pen tops
Sticky sticks from lollipops

Bits of dust
Specks of dirt
Buttons from forgotten shirts

Chocolate wrappers
Snotty tissues
Newspaper back issues

Piles of fluff
Odd shoes
Pet rabbit do-dos

Penny coins
Bottle caps
Torn-up Tube maps

Shopping receipts from yesteryear
Balls of wax from Grandad's ear . . .

Safety pins
Drawing pins
Fingernails and hard skin

Bubble gum
Sucked sweets
Chewed-up dog treats

Crisp packets
Rusty screws
Bills that are overdue

Dental floss
Locks of hair
Labels from your underwear

Apple cores
Paper clips
Mouldy black and green chips

Half-eaten sausage rolls
Stuff them down the black hole

You got rubbish want to hide it?
Where's the secret place to slide it?
Down the side of the sofa

I Won't Eat Snails!

I don't want snails for dinner
Or lurking in my lunch
Their yucky bodies squish and squelch
Their shells crack with a crunch
In France they may adore them
But I'm in England now
So remove them from the table
I won't eat snails!

I don't want snails for breakfast
No antennae with my tea
Return them to the garden
Drop them by the nearest tree
You can drag me to the station
Tie me helpless to the rails
But keep molluscs off the menu
I won't eat snails!

I don't want snails in sandwiches
They're too terrible on toast
In marinades on barbecues
Or served with Sunday roast
I'll strip down to my underpants
In rain, snow, sleet and hail
But one delicacy's not for me
I won't eat snails!

I don't want snails for supper
For pudding or for sweet
I don't regard a gastropod
In garlic as a treat
I can't consume a creature
Oozing slippery, slimy trails
Though for a dare I'd bite a bear
I won't eat snails!

Pay me sack loads of money
Or immerse them in honey
Still I won't eat snails!

Beware the Pamplemousse!

(In France they have a cool word for grapefruit: pamplemousse. *I imagine it to be a rather mean and unfriendly fruit.)*

I'm a sour, round monster
The deadly Pamplemousse
Stinging, tingling your tongue with my acidic juice
The Demon from the Darkside living in your fruit bowl
Don't use me as a doorstop
Don't use me as a football

My shiny, dimpled, bumpy body's brightly coloured yellow
Though many fruits are sweet and cute
I'm a nasty, noxious fellow
You may lick your lips for strawberries
Or for bananas
But I'm about as popular as a sea full of piranhas

Rarely in your five a day whether red or pink or white
I'll upset the toughest tummy, always looking for a fight
Buy me from the supermarket
Evil, mean and bitter
Beware the Pamplemousse
The heaviest of heavy hitters

People peel me to reveal me
And rip and tear my skin
Then separate my segments
But I'll bite back to win
I'll cause you tooth decay
I'll squirt into your eyes
"Beware the Pamplemousse"
Is my chilling battle cry

I'm the terrifying creature
That children never choose
So plan your escape route
From this gruesome grapefruit
And . . .
Beware the Pamplemousse

Our Fridge Door

Our fridge door is a voyage of discovery
Postcards from Peru, Australia and Italy
Four family photos from a day at London Zoo
Including penguins, pandas, parrots (but not kangaroos)
Some emergency phone numbers in case we need them
A note saying "Neighbour's cats: don't forget to feed them!"

There's a letter for my brother about a job interview
And one from the dentist as his check-up is now due
A school timetable, a map of Birmingham
A tiny squashed spider, sticky fingerprints from jam
There's a souvenir magnet picturing Tower Bridge
Yes all this super stuff's stuck onto our fridge

Our fridge door is a voyage of discovery
A voucher for deodorant, a chicken curry recipe
You'll spot the twelve times table ('cause that's what I'm learning)
A reminder that my new shoes need returning
Last year's Christmas shopping list containing loads of items
Impossible to understand through Mum's messy writing

A used cinema ticket, an old electric bill
Instructions for my dad on how to take his purple pills
A drawing of my sister in which
 her head's shaped like a potato
To answer life's great mysteries
 see our refrigerator
So don't search on the Internet
 as you no longer need it
Just come into our kitchen,
 find our fridge door
 and then read it

I Swallowed a Whale

Yesterday I swallowed a whale
Head, body, blubber, fins and tail
Like Jonah's story in reverse
Or swallowing a fly but worse
In the ocean for a swim
My mouth opened, it zoomed in
Friends tell me I'm pale and frail
Why? I swallowed a whale

One less beast's in the Atlantic
Now my stomach's grown gigantic
Drives me crazy, drives me nuts
Bouncing, bumping round my guts
Splashing, sploshing in my belly
A jumping, jiggling bowl of jelly
And I broke my set of bathroom scales
Because I swallowed a whale

"Enough!" I'm pleading with the vet
"Please remove then lose this pet!"
Everybody says to me
"There are plenty more fish in the sea"
(Though actually a whale's a mammal
Related not to cod but camel)
I should have swallowed an ant, a beetle,
    a worm, a spider, a slug or a snail
Instead
I swallowed a whale